MARY SHELLEY'S

FRANKENSTEIN

THE GRAPHIC NOVEL

illustrated by Frazer Irving
script by Gary Reed

PUFFIN BOOKS

Visit us at www.abdopub.com

Spotlight, a division of ABDO Publishing Company, is a distributor of high quality reinforced library bound editions for schools and libraries.

This library bound edition is published by arrangement with Penguin Young Readers Group, a member of Penguin Group (USA) Inc.

Library of Congress Cataloging-In-Publication Data

PUFFIN BOOKS
Published by the Penguin Group
Penguin Young Readers Group,
345 Hudson Street, New York, NY 10014 U.S.A.

Frankenstein Graphic Novel first published by Puffin Books, a division of Penguin Young Readers Group, 2005

A Byron Preiss Book
Byron Preiss Visual Publications
24 West 25th Street, New York, NY 10010

Illustrated by Frazer Irving
Script by Gary Reed
Lettering by Ryan Yount
Series Editor: Dwight Jon Zimmerman
Series Assistant Editor: April Isaacs
Interior design by M. Postawa and Gilda Hannah
Cover design by M. Postawa

Puffin Books ISBN 0-14-240407-1
ISBN: 1-59961-116-3 Reinforced Library Bound Edition

All Spotlight books are reinforced library binding and manufactured in the United States of America.

MARY SHELLEY'S

FRANKENSTEIN

THE LOGBOOK OF CAPTAIN ROBERT WALTON FROM THE SHIP, THE *ARCHANGEL*.

"IT HAS BEEN *SIX MONTHS* SINCE OUR VOYAGE BEGAN. WE HAD SET OUT TO DISCOVER THE SECRETS OF THE *ARCTIC*.

"INSTEAD, WE ARE A *PRISONER* OF THE ICE THAT SQUEEZES US FROM ALL SIDES.

"FOR WEEKS WE HAVE BEEN TRAPPED IN THIS DESOLATE *SPOT*.

"FROM HERE, THE WORLD SEEMS TO HAVE NO LIFE, ONLY *ICE*.

"THEN I SAW *SOMETHING* THAT I SHOULD NOT HAVE SEEN HERE."

6

"I SAT WITH HIM FOR DAYS. HE *SLEPT*...

"...MOST OF THE TIME.

"HE WOULD WAKE OCCASIONALLY AND CALL OUT *NAMES*...

...ELIZABETH...

...WILLIAM...

...HENRY...

"AND SOMETIMES HE WOULD SOB WITH *GRIEF*."

"AT TIMES, HE SEEMED *WELL* AND CARRIED ON NORMAL *CONVERSATION*.

"IT IS APPARENT THAT HE IS WELL EDUCATED... A MAN OF *SCIENCE*.

"WHEN I ASKED HIM *WHY* HE WAS OUT ON THE ICE, HIS ANSWER *SURPRISED* ME."

I MUST FIND THE DEMON. I MUST *DESTROY* HIM.

7

8

9

"BECAUSE OF MY FATHER'S COMMITMENT TO WORK, HE DID NOT MARRY EARLY.

"WHEN MY FATHER'S BEST FRIEND DIED, HE LEFT A DAUGHTER, CAROLINE. MY FATHER TOOK HER IN.

"EVEN THOUGH THERE WAS A CONSIDERABLE DIFFERENCE IN AGES BETWEEN MY FATHER AND CAROLINE, THEY EVENTUALLY FELL IN LOVE.

"THEY MARRIED AND SOON AFTER, I WAS BORN."

"MY MOTHER TOOK IN A YOUNG GIRL, *ELIZABETH*, WHO WAS LIVING WITH PEASANTS. MOTHER SAID SHE WAS A PRESENT FOR ME. AND I ALWAYS FELT SHE WAS MINE AND WOULD BE FOREVER.

"ELIZABETH JOINED OUR *FAMILY*. AT FIRST, SHE WAS LIKE A *SISTER* TO ME.

"LATER, SHE WOULD BECOME SO MUCH *MORE*.

"AND THEN MY BROTHER, WILLIAM, WAS BORN. SWEET, ADORABLE *WILLIAM*. IT WAS, AS I SAID, A PERFECT CHILDHOOD."

"I ATTENDED SCHOOL AND DID WELL, BUT I DID NOT MAKE MANY FRIENDS THERE.

"I WAS A *SERIOUS STUDENT* AND WAS NOT INTERESTED IN ACTIVITIES OUTSIDE OF LEARNING.

"THE ONLY FRIEND I MADE WAS *HENRY CLERVAL*. HE HAD VERY DIFFERENT INTERESTS THAN I DID, YET WE FOUND MUCH IN *COMMON*.

"WE BOTH LIKED TO EXPLORE THE *WONDERS OF THE WORLD*. HE PREFERRED TALES OF DRAMA AND HEROES... WHILE I HAD MORE INTEREST IN NATURE AND SCIENCE."

"MY FATHER MADE SURE TO SUPPLY ME WITH ENOUGH *BOOKS* TO FULFILL MY PASSION FOR LEARNING."

"I WAS CAPTIVATED BY THE *MYSTERIES* OF LIFE AND HOW THE WORLD WORKED."

"WHEN I SAW THE POWERFUL FORCE OF *LIGHTNING* AND THE DESTRUCTION THAT IT COULD CAUSE, I KNEW THAT SCIENCE WOULD BE MY *FUTURE*."

"I HAD TO KNOW HOW *EVERYTHING* WORKED, HOW EVERYTHING CAME INTO BEING."

"I COULD NOT LEAVE A *QUESTION* UNANSWERED."

14

AND THEN *TRAGEDY* STRUCK, THE FIRST TRAGEDY I HAD EVER FACED.

"WHEN I LOOK BACK NOW, I REALIZE IT WAS AT THAT *MOMENT* THAT MY LIFE BEGAN ITS TWISTED PATH OF *MISERY*.

"MY PERFECT CHILDHOOD HAD *ENDED*.

"MY MOTHER *DIED*."

"WALDMAN **ENCOURAGED** MY BURNING PASSION TO LEARN ABOUT LIFE. HE LOANED ME ALL OF HIS **BOOKS**.

"I STUDIED THE WORKS OF SCIENTISTS FROM AROUND THE **WORLD**.

"FOR TWO YEARS, I DID NOTHING BUT **STUDY**. I MADE NO RETURN HOME.

"PROFESSOR WALDMAN WAS SO IMPRESSED THAT HE GAVE ME MY OWN **LABORATORY** WITH LIVING QUARTERS TO CONTINUE MY STUDIES."

"I STUDIED HOW LIFE WORKED... AND WHAT CAUSED *DEATH*.

"I SAW THAT EVEN LIFE WAS MADE OF CHEMICALS AND HOW CHEMISTRY COULD UNLOCK MANY *SECRETS*.

"I HAD A PASSION TO UNCOVER THE *MYSTERIES* OF THE HUMAN BODY.

"AND SLOWLY, I BEGAN TO DEVELOP AN *IDEA*. AN IDEA THAT WOULD SOLVE THE RIDDLE OF LIFE."

"I DESIGNED MY *CREATION* TO BE LARGE, OVER EIGHT FEET TALL.
"HE WAS TO BE A *SYMBOL* FOR THE POWER OF SCIENCE.
"I USED THE *ALLOWANCE* MY FATHER GAVE ME.
"AND *STOLE* WHAT I COULD NOT AFFORD.
"SCIENCE WOULD RISE ABOVE *NATURE*...
"...SCIENCE WOULD DETERMINE *LIFE*...
"...*AND DEATH*."

24

"IT WAS A DREARY NIGHT IN *NOVEMBER* WHEN I FINISHED.

"I COLLAPSED IN *EXHAUSTION.*

"ALL I COULD DO THEN WAS *WAIT...*

"...WAIT TO SEE IF MY CREATION WOULD STIR WITH *LIFE.*"

"I WAITED WITH ANXIOUS *AGONY*.

"THEN... THEN, ITS EYES *OPENED*.

"I HEARD A *DEEP BREATH*... A GULPING BREATH...

"...AND MY CREATION... MY *PERFECT CREATION*...

"...WAS *ALIVE!*"

27

"IT *CONVULSED*.

"ITS BODY SHOOK AS IF JOLTED WITH *ELECTRICITY*.

"LIMBS TWISTED... THE LIPS *SNARLED*...

"YELLOW WATERY *EYES* LOOKED OUT FROM—

"MY GOD! WHAT HAD I *DONE!?*"

29

"I COULD HEAR ITS RASPY BREATH...
"...AND ITS UNSTEADY STEPS.
"AND WHEN IT CAME TO ME...
"I KNEW I HAD NOT CREATED A MAN..."
"...BUT A MONSTER!"

31

"I *FLED.*

"I RAN FROM MY MONTHS OF *HARD WORK.*

"I DIDN'T KNOW *WHERE* TO RUN...

"BUT I HAD TO GET AWAY... *ANYWHERE*... JUST AWAY.".

"FEVER CAPTURED MY BODY AND I RETREATED INTO A DEEP *SLEEP*.

"*SPRING* CAME AND WENT.

"HENRY THOUGHT IT WAS *NIGHTMARES*.

"WHEN SUMMER CAME, HENRY WAS STILL THERE. HE WAS SUCH A *GOOD FRIEND* TO NURSE ME BACK TO HEALTH."

36

"A STORM *RAGED*, BUT I WAS UNABLE TO *REST*.

"BEFORE ENTERING THE CITY, I HAD TO SEE FOR MYSELF WHERE WILLIAM HAD BEEN *MURDERED*.

"I HAD RETURNED TO THE LAND THAT WAS MY *HOME*.

"I HAD NO DESIRE TO EVER *LEAVE* AGAIN."

"JUSTINE PAID THE *PRICE* FOR MY MISTAKE.

"HOW COULD I *LIVE* WITH MYSELF NOW...?

"IT WAS IF MY OWN *HANDS* HAD COMMITTED THE DEED."

"OUR HOUSE WAS A HOUSE OF *MOURNING*.

"IMAGES OF WILLIAM AND JUSTINE FLOATED IN MY *HEAD*.

"AND I WAS PARALYZED WITH *FEAR* OF THAT MONSTER...

"ONLY TO BE REPLACED BY MY *CREATION*.

"...WONDERING WHO WOULD BE *NEXT*?"

"THE *TORMENT* OF BEING AROUND MY *FAMILY* WAS TOO MUCH.

"THEY *GRIEVED* FOR DEATHS I HAD CAUSED.

"I *RETREATED* TO THE MOUNTAINS."

"NOT EVEN THE *BEAUTY* OF THE MOUNTAINS COULD IMPROVE MY MISERY.

"AS A CHILD, I OFTEN CAME HERE TO *DREAM* OF HOW I WOULD BECOME A GREAT SCIENTIST.

"INSTEAD, I HAD TO FACE THE FACT THAT I WAS A *MURDERER*."

"THEN I SAW A *MAN* IN THE DISTANCE.

"HE WAS RACING TOWARDS ME WITH SUPERHUMAN *SPEED*.

"IT WAS A *LARGE MAN*.

"THEN I SAW IT WAS NOT A MAN AT ALL.

"IT WAS THE *CREATURE!*

"*MY* CREATURE!"

48

"THE NOISE AND LIGHTS OF THE CITY HAD *SCARED* ME.

"I ESCAPED INTO THE DARKNESS OF THE *FOREST*.

"EVERYTHING WAS *NEW* TO ME... SIGHTS, SOUNDS, AND SMELLS.

"MY BODY WAS *SORE* AND IT HURT WHEN I SWALLOWED.

"I SOON DISCOVERED HOW *WATER* WOULD SOOTHE MY THROAT."

"I BEGIN TO *ENJOY* THESE NEW SENSATIONS.

"I LOOKED FORWARD TO THE *SUN* EACH MORNING WITH ITS LIGHT AND HEAT.

"WHEN I CAME ACROSS A LIGHT BURNING AT *NIGHT*...

"...I FOUND FIRE THAT WAS LEFT BY WANDERING *BEGGARS*."

"BUT EVEN WITH THE FIRE, THE COLD OF THE NIGHT WAS **UNBEARABLE.**

"AND THE ONLY **FOOD** I FOUND WERE BERRIES AND NUTS.

"I KNEW I HAD TO LEAVE THE FOREST IF I WANTED TO **SURVIVE.**

"I WAS DELIGHTED WHEN I CAME ACROSS A **SMALL TOWN.**

"I FELT A SENSE OF JOY... A SENSE OF **BELONGING.** I WOULD NOT BE ALONE ANYMORE."

"WHAT HAD I DONE TO DESERVE SUCH *TREATMENT*? I FLED BACK INTO THE WOODS.

"I *RAN* UNTIL I COULDN'T RUN ANY MORE.

"WHEN I SAW THE *HUT* IN THE DARKNESS, I MADE SURE THERE WERE NO PEOPLE AROUND.

"IT WAS WARM AND *DRY* INSIDE.

"FOR THE FIRST TIME, I FELT AT *PEACE*.

"AND I *SLEPT* FOR THE LONGEST TIME I COULD REMEMBER."

"I SPENT EVERY *HOUR* WATCHING THEM. I *LEARNED* A GREAT DEAL. THE OLD MAN, WHO THEY CALLED FATHER, WAS *BLIND*.

"THE GENTLE SOUL WAS AGATHA. SHE HAD A VOICE LIKE AN *ANGEL*. AND THE SON WAS CALLED FELIX.

"I LISTENED AND WATCHED AS THEY TALKED TO EACH OTHER. I PICKED UP THE *LANGUAGE* AS IF IT WERE A LOST ART...

"I PRACTICED MY SIMPLE *WORDS* AT NIGHT WHEN I HAD LEFT THE COTTAGE TO EAT."

"I WAITED ANXIOUSLY THE NEXT *MORNING* TO SEE THEM DISCOVER THE CHOPPED WOOD.

"THEY WERE *SURPRISED* AND I BECAME SCARED. I THOUGHT THEY MIGHT START SEARCHING AND *DISCOVER* ME.

"BUT THEY *ACCEPTED* THE WOOD WITHOUT SEARCHING.

"AND I WAS SO PLEASED WITH MYSELF. I HAD MADE ANOTHER PERSON *HAPPY*."

62

"THEN I DARED TO READ THE *PAPERS* THAT WERE IN YOUR *COAT* THAT I TOOK THE NIGHT I WAS BORN.

"I *WEPT* WHEN I READ THEM. THE PAPERS REVEALED THE *TRUTH* ABOUT ME... AND ABOUT YOU.

"I REALIZED YOU WERE MY *FATHER*... AND YET YOU *ABANDONED* ME."

"ONE DAY, THE FAMILY LEFT HOME... EXCEPT FOR THE *OLD BLIND MAN*.

"HE WOULD NOT JUDGE ME ON MY *APPEARANCE* ALONE.

"I DARED TO MEET HIM... TO *TALK* WITH HIM.

"I WOULD FINALLY TALK TO ANOTHER *HUMAN*... MAN TO MAN.

"HE *INVITED* ME IN WITHOUT HESITATION."

69

"WHAT HAD I DONE TO BE TREATED SO CRUELLY?
"IT WAS THEN THAT I DECIDED...
"I WOULD TREAT MANKIND AS IT TREATED ME...
"...WITH HATRED!"

"I REREAD YOUR *JOURNAL*.

"THOUGH YOU WERE MY CREATOR... MY *'FATHER'*...

"...IT WAS *YOU* WHO FIRST TURNED *AWAY* FROM ME."

72

"I COULD NOT LET THE GIRL *DROWN*, SO I *SAVED* HER.

"YET AGAIN, I RECEIVED ONLY *PAIN* FOR MY ACTIONS.

"MANKIND WOULD *NOT ACCEPT ME*."

74

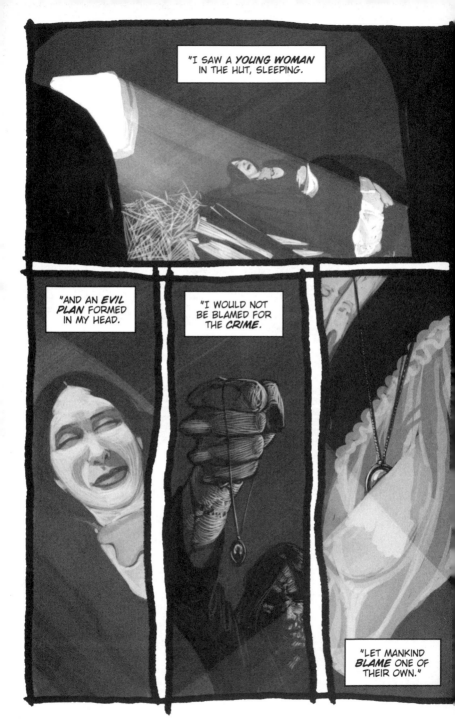

"I SAW A *YOUNG WOMAN* IN THE HUT, SLEEPING.

"AND AN *EVIL PLAN* FORMED IN MY HEAD.

"I WOULD NOT BE BLAMED FOR THE *CRIME*.

"LET MANKIND *BLAME* ONE OF THEIR OWN."

83

84

"HENRY AND I SET SAIL FOR *ENGLAND*.

"IN ENGLAND, THERE WERE *GREAT SCIENTISTS* WHO MIGHT HAVE SOME OF THE ANSWERS TO WHAT WENT *WRONG* WITH MY CREATION.

"BUT I KNEW IN MY HEART, I HAD TO GET AWAY FROM MY FATHER AND ELIZABETH TO COMPLETE MY *TERRIBLE TASK*."

"ELIZABETH. IT SEEMS SO LONG AGO THAT I WAS TO FINISH SCHOOL...

"...AND THEN WE WOULD BE *MARRIED*...

"...SETTLE DOWN TO A *COMFORTABLE LIFE*.

"BUT MY WORK, MY *CREATION*, HAD CHANGED THAT.

"IT HAD CHANGED *EVERYTHING*."

"THE GREAT CITY OF **LONDON** HELD A GREAT DEAL OF **PROMISE**.

"I ARRANGED TO MEET WITH MANY OF THE **TOP SCIENTISTS** AT CAMBRIDGE, OXFORD, AND OTHERS.

"MY **REPUTATION** AS A GIFTED STUDENT SERVED ME WELL.

"I MET WITH SOME OF THE MOST BRILLIANT MINDS OF **SCIENCE**."

90

"I FOUND A **DESOLATE ISLAND** THAT WAS PERFECT.

"IT WAS **ISOLATED** AND HAD NO LIFE EXCEPT FOR ME...

"...AND SOON, THE BEING I WOULD **CREATE**."

96

"I WAS NEARLY FINISHED. SHE WOULD *LIVE* ONCE I PERFORMED THE *FINAL STEP*.

"SOMETIMES, I SAW *SHADOWS* OUTSIDE.

"THE *MONSTER* HAD COME TO MY ISLAND."

99

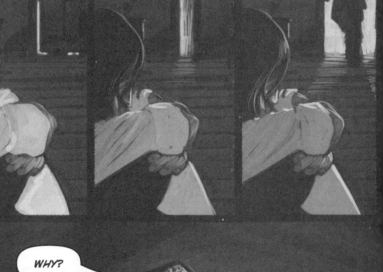

"IN THE BLACKNESS OF THE SEA, I CAST AWAY MY *ABANDONED CREATION*.

"THE *ORDEAL* WAS OVER.

"I ALLOWED *SLEEP* TO WASH OVER ME."

114

"I NEVER SAW ELIZABETH SO *HAPPY*.

"BUT I COULD NOT TELL HER OF MY *TERRIBLE SECRET*.

"NOR COULD I TELL HER OF THE *REVENGE* THE MONSTER PLANNED... TO KILL ME ON OUR WEDDING NIGHT.

"BUT THAT COULD ALL *WAIT*.

"I DIDN'T WANT ANYTHING TO PREVENT HER *JOY*."

"SO, ALTHOUGH I APPEARED TO OTHERS IN *HIGH SPIRITS*...

"...AND I REJOICED IN ELIZABETH'S *DELIGHT*...

"I KNEW WHAT AWAITED *ME*.

"THE MONSTER AND I WOULD MEET *TONIGHT*."

"HE SAID, 'I WILL SEE YOU ON YOUR WEDDING NIGHT.'"
"NOW I KNEW...
"HE NEVER MEANT ME...
"...IT WAS ELIZABETH!"

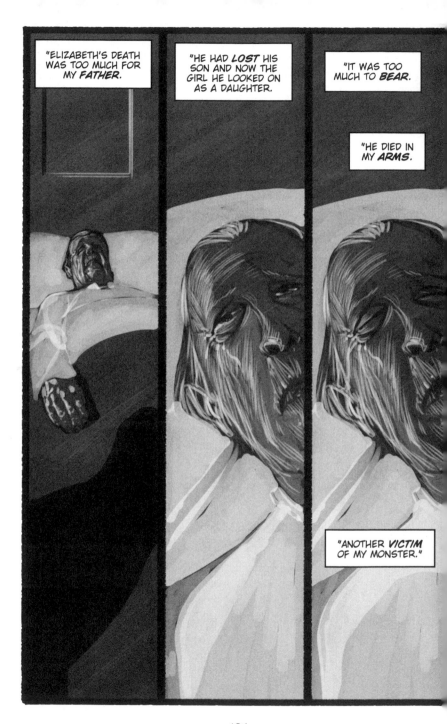

"ELIZABETH'S DEATH WAS TOO MUCH FOR MY *FATHER*.

"HE HAD *LOST* HIS SON AND NOW THE GIRL HE LOOKED ON AS A DAUGHTER.

"IT WAS TOO MUCH TO *BEAR*.

"HE DIED IN MY *ARMS*.

"ANOTHER *VICTIM* OF MY MONSTER."

127

"THE WEATHER WAS CHANGING. WARM WEATHER WAS MELTING THE ICE.
"I WOULD HAVE TO CATCH IT SOON... BEFORE THE ICE BROKE UP.
"THEN...
"I SAW IT!"

"MY EYES TEARED FROM THE COLD AND FROM THE *RELIEF* THAT I FELT.

"I WOULD CATCH IT. MY *TORMENT* WAS NEARLY OVER!

"ONE OF US, IF NOT BOTH, WOULD *DIE*."

"GONE. IT WAS *GONE*.

"I COULD *TRAVEL* NO FURTHER.

"THE COLD TOOK HOLD OF ME AND THEN I SAW YOUR *SHIP*.

"YOU WERE MY *LAST HOPE*, MY ONLY CHANCE AT SURVIVAL SO THAT I COULD CONTINUE MY QUEST."

NOW YOU KNOW WHY I CANNOT GO *BACK*... WHY I MUST STAY AND *END* THAT WHICH I CREATED.

THE LOGBOOK OF *CAPTAIN ROBERT WALTON.*

"AFTER FRANKENSTEIN FINISHED HIS *NARRATION*, HE COLLAPSED AGAIN INTO A DEEP SLEEP. THE SHIP'S *DOCTOR* DIDN'T EXPECT HIM TO LIVE VERY LONG.

"ALTHOUGH I WISHED TO REMAIN IN THIS *FROZEN WILDERNESS* FOR FRANKENSTEIN'S SAKE, MY MEN HAD *OTHER IDEAS*."

"FRANKENSTEIN SLIPPED INTO A *COMA*."

"I HOPED THAT PERHAPS HE WOULD FIND *PEACE* NOW... PEACE WITH HIMSELF AND PEACE WITH HIS *VENGEANCE*."

"I STAYED WITH HIM FOR A FEW HOURS... UNTIL I HEARD HIS *LAST BREATH*.

"VICTOR FRANKENSTEIN WAS *DEAD*."

"FIRST LIGHT OF THE NEXT MORNING BROUGHT A REALIZATION THAT IT WAS TO BE THE LAST DAY OF MY *JOURNEY*.

"ALTHOUGH I FEEL I HAVE *FAILED* ON MY MISSION, I THINK OF FRANKENSTEIN...

"...AND MAYBE THAT SOME THINGS SHOULD NOT BE *ATTEMPTED*.

WHA—???

"THE *MONSTER!* THE MONSTER WAS AT FRANKENSTEIN'S DEATHBED.

"I BELIEVED EVERY WORD OF FRANKENSTEIN... BUT TO ACTUALLY *SEE* THE CREATURE!"

"AND WITH A GREAT *LEAP*, THE MONSTER BOUNDED ONTO THE ICE.

"I FELT A STRANGE SENSE OF SADNESS FOR THE CREATURE.

"HE WAS BIGGER, STRONGER, FASTER, AND PERHAPS MORE *INTELLECTUAL* THAN MOST MEN.

"YET, HE WAS *INFERIOR* BECAUSE HE WAS MADE BY ANOTHER MAN."

"THE CREATURE HAD WANTED *LITTLE* IN LIFE...

"ALTHOUGH HIS CREATOR HAD WANTED SO *MUCH*.

"BOTH HAD *FAILED*."

"LEAVING BEHIND A *CREATOR* AND HIS *CREATION*.

"ONLY DEATH COULD BRING THEM *TOGETHER*."

THE END